The Best Of Alex 2006

Charles Peattie & Russell Taylor

Masterley Publishing

The Best Of
Alex
2006

First published by MASTERLEY PUBLISHING

Layout and Artwork: Jain Spero

ISBN-10: 1-85375-605-9
ISBN-13: 978-185375-605-4

"FTSE indices provide a measure of securities performance for everyone working across global markets, while Mondo Visione's publications tell you just about everything you need to know about what's happening in exchanges and trading venues in all the financial capitals of the world. But no, we can't tell you how to get the best table in the best restaurants - for that you'll have to speak to Alex! Both organisations wish Alex and his colleagues much success in 2007."

FOREWORD

There's no doubt about it – Alex is getting older. He's already begun voicing the fortysomething's traditional trio of gripes about working in the modern financial world (longer hours, less money, no fun) and a slot on Grumpy Old Men beckons. And to make him even more aware of his rapidly evaporating youth this year's crop of summer interns includes not only HRH Prince William but also one Christopher Masterley, Alex's seventeen year old son.

Oh, and just in case you thought a midlife crisis wasn't imminent, he's started having an affair (though at the request of some of our male readers we must point out that the notion of office romances is highly fanciful and that if our public - who may or may not include these men's wives - wish to read a more realistic scenario about the business world they should turn to pages 33 - 37 which find Alex and Clive hobnobbing with centaurs and satyrs in Narnia).

Shocked as we are by Alex's behaviour we are curious to see what develops. Where might he be by next year's annual? Perhaps he will have dumped Penny, used his wealth to set himself up with a trophy girlfriend half his age, be living in a designer pad in Islington with walls full of modern art, riding a motorbike, hanging out in nightclubs. All the classic ingredients of the sad, born-again bachelor lifestyle. Except we're struggling to work out what exactly is "sad" about it all..

Of course inflicting the miseries of middle age upon Alex might just be our way of denying our own advancing years - using him as a sort of Picture of Dorian Gray, becoming corpulent and crotchety, while we, his unseen creators, remain eternally youthful and angst-free.

Which would all be very well, except that we keep meeting young investment bankers who tell us they have been reading Alex since their childhood. Not only does this make us feel uncomfortably ancient but - worse still - a failure as satirists. If you guys imbibed Alex jokes with your mother's milk why on earth did you end up working in the City? The idea was to put you off…

There's just no understanding young people these days.

Charles Peattie and Russell Taylor

① **Alex** (investment banker)
② **Clive** (Alex's colleague and sometime boss)
③ **Penny** (Alex's wife)
④ **Christopher** (their son)
⑤ **Bridget** (Cive's wife)
⑥ **Rupert** (senior director)
⑦ **Cyrus** (new boss from America)
⑧ **Christian** (eurotrash trainee)
⑨ **Carolyn** (client of Alex - and something more)

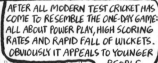

Alex PEATTIE + TAYLOR

SO, ALEX, WHAT DO YOU THINK OF THESE CALLS FOR TEST MATCHES TO BE REDUCED TO FOUR DAYS' DURATION?

I CAN SEE THE LOGIC OF IT...

AFTER ALL MODERN TEST CRICKET HAS COME TO RESEMBLE THE ONE-DAY GAME: ALL ABOUT POWER PLAY, HIGH SCORING RATES AND RAPID FALL OF WICKETS. OBVIOUSLY IT APPEALS TO YOUNGER PEOPLE...

BUT AS SOMEONE OF THE OLDER GENERATION I FEEL IT WOULD BE A SHAME TO LOSE THE FIVE-DAY GAME AND ALL THE FINESSE, STRATAGEMS AND SUBTLETIES ASSOCIATED WITH IT...

SUCH AS LETTING THE GRADUATE TRAINEE HOST THE CORPORATE BOX ON THE FIFTH DAY? QUITE - WHEN THE CHANCES ARE THERE'LL BE NO PLAY TO WATCH...

email: alex-cartoon @ etgate.co.uk

Alex PEATTIE + TAYLOR

IN LIGHT OF THE LONDON BOMBS LAST MONTH SECURITY PROCEDURES HAVE BEEN TIGHTENED UP...

IT'S LONG BEEN IMPOSSIBLE TO GET FIRE-ARMS ABOARD A PLANE BUT POLICE ARE NOW HAVING TO BE EXTRA VIGILANT ABOUT THE POSSIBILITY OF WEAPONS CACHES BEING TRANSPORTED BY ROAD...

OF COURSE IT LEADS TO THE ODD BLAMELESS MOTORIST BEING INCONVENIENCED BUT ONE JUST HAS TO THINK OF THE DOZENS OF INNOCENT LIVES IT COULD SAVE...

LIKE ALL THOSE PHEASANTS YOU WERE PLANNING TO SHOOT TODAY...

BUT I RELY ON YOU TO DRIVE MY SHOTGUNS UP HERE... TELL THE POLICE TO RELEASE YOU IMMEDIATELY...

WELCOME TO SCOTLAND

email: alex-cartoon @ etgate.co.uk

Alex PEATTIE + TAYLOR

I'M SO GLAD THE SHOOTING SEASON'S STARTED AGAIN...IT'S AN IMPORTANT PART OF THE CORPORATE CALENDAR.

YES, I'M UP HERE ON A GROUSE MOOR IN SCOTLAND... THE BEATERS JUST SENT A FEW BIRDS UP OVER US...

NO...NO GREAT LUCK SO FAR... IT'S A BIT FRUSTRATING, BUT I'M HOPING FOR GREATER SUCCESS ON THE NEXT DRIVE...

THESE DRIVES BETWEEN SITES ARE THE ONLY BITS ALEX SEEMS TO ENJOY...

YES. IT'S TOUGH FOR ASSIDUOUS NETWORKERS LIKE HIM: HAVING TO SPEND SO MUCH TIME STANDING IN A FIELD ON THEIR OWN...

email: alex-cartoon @ etgate.co.uk

Alex PEATTIE + TAYLOR

MEGABANK

IT'S FUNNY HOW THE BANK'S ATTITUDE TO ITS SMOKERS HAS CHANGED OVER THE YEARS.

ONCE WE WERE ALLOWED TO SMOKE AT OUR DESKS, THEN WE WERE BANISHED TO A SMOKING ROOM, THEN MADE TO STAND OUTSIDE THE BUILDING...

NOW WE HAVE TO GO ELSEWHERE SO WE DON'T MAKE A BAD IMPRESSION ON VISITING CLIENTS...

OF COURSE IT'S NO COINCIDENCE THAT ALL THIS HAS ACCOMPANIED THE RISE IN POWER OF THE MIDDLE OFFICE - THOSE BUREAUCRATIC BUSYBODIES WHO TRY TO CONTROL EVERY ASPECT OF OUR LIVES...

YES.

LIKE COMPLIANCE WHO HAVE BANNED VARIOUS DEPART-MENTS FROM TALKING TO EACH OTHER...

SO IT'S HANDY HAVING A BONA FIDE EXCUSE TO SLIP ROUND THE CORNER FOR AN OFF-THE-RECORD CHAT...

CLICK

OKAY...WHAT DEALS ARE YOU WORKING ON?

email: alex-cartoon @ etgate.co.uk

Alex PEATTIE + TAYLOR

THE CITY PRIDES ITSELF ON ITS POLICIES TO PROTECT WOMEN'S RIGHTS IN THE WORKPLACE...

BUT THE REALITY IS THAT THERE ARE STILL AREAS WHERE A MAN'S EARNING CAPACITY CONSIDERABLY EXCEEDS THAT OF HIS FEMALE COLLEAGUES...

SO OFTEN ONE'S EFFORTS AS A WOMAN ARE DELIBERATELY OVERLOOKED BY A MALE BOSS. I MEAN, WHEN YOU CONSIDER HOW HARD I'VE WORKED OVER RECENT WEEKS...

WHAT, NOT AT ALL...?

EXACTLY. I'VE TOTALLY SLACKED OFF BECAUSE I'VE GOT A NEW JOB TO GO TO AND WANT TO GET MADE REDUNDANT...

BUT THEY'RE ALL TOO SCARED TO DO IT TO US. IT'S SO UNFAIR...

Alex PEATTIE + TAYLOR

THE PROBLEM WITH GETTING THROUGH TO A CLIENT BY PHONE IS ONE NEVER KNOWS WHEN HE'S GOING TO BE AT HIS DESK...

WHICH IS WHY E-MAIL IS A GODSEND TO SALES PEOPLE LIKE US...THESE DAYS WE CAN JUST SEND ALL OUR IDEAS THROUGH TO THE CLIENT FOR HIM TO LOOK AT WHEN HE'S GOT THE TIME...

AND OF COURSE THERE'S THE FACILITY THAT LETS US KNOW IF AND WHEN HE'S READ THEM...

PING

WHAT?! A BATCH OF MY E-MAILS HAS JUST COME BACK FROM A CLIENT AUTO-DELETED AND UNREAD...

EXCELLENT. SO AT LEAST YOU KNOW HE'S AT HIS DESK... NOW'S THE TIME TO CATCH HIM ON THE PHONE AND BLAG HIM INTO DOING SOME BUSINESS.

GOOD IDEA...

Alex PEATTIE + TAYLOR

THIS LATEST DIRECTIVE ON AVOIDING NEGATIVE ETHNIC ASSOCIATIONS IN USE OF LANGUAGE REALLY IS ABSURD.

LOOK, ALEX, THE FOCUS OF THE BUSINESS WORLD IS SHIFTING AWAY FROM EUROPE AND THE UNITED STATES AND INCREASINGLY TOWARDS INDIA AND CHINA...

WE MUST BE SENSITIVE TO OUR NEW ASIAN TRADING PARTNERS AND ESCHEW TERMINOLOGY THAT MIGHT HAVE PEJORATIVE RACIAL OR CULTURAL OVERTONES TO THEM.

WHICH IS WHY "CHINESE WALLS" ARE TO BE RENAMED "INFORMATION BARRIERS".

BECAUSE ONE WOULDN'T WANT TO IMPLY ANYONE OUT THERE HAD ANY RESPECT FOR COMPLIANCE REGULATIONS?

ER, YES... I MEAN, NO... ER... ER...

Alex PEATTIE + TAYLOR

SO YOU'RE ON A WALKING HOLIDAY IN SCOTLAND, PENNY?

YES, WE'VE RENTED AN OLD CROFTER'S COTTAGE IN THE HIGHLANDS...

I MUST ADMIT I WOULDN'T HAVE EXPECTED SUCH A NOTED WORKAHOLIC AS ALEX TO BE THAT KEEN ON OUTDOOR PURSUITS...

WELL, HE WASN'T REALLY AT THE BEGINNING

BUT SINCE THEN HE'S GOT MUCH MORE INTO IT. IT WAS HIM THAT PERSUADED US TO GET UP AT 6 AM TO COME ON THIS 20 MILE HIKE UP A MOUNTAIN...

THIS IS THE ONLY PLACE ROUND HERE HE CAN GET A SIGNAL ON HIS BLACKBERRY...

15

16

Alex — PEATTIE + TAYLOR

SO, RUPERT, HAS THE BANK'S SUMMER INTERNAL REORGANISATION BEEN A SUCCESS?

I THINK SO, CLIVE.

OF COURSE MUCH OF IT IS JUST TO CONFORM WITH THE LATEST COMPLIANCE EDICTS BANNING VARIOUS DEPARTMENTS FROM TALKING TO VARIOUS OTHERS...

STILL, IT ALL CREATES THE RIGHT IMPRESSION ON PEOPLE RETURNING FROM THEIR SUMMER HOLIDAYS—THAT MANAGEMENT HAS BEEN TAKING ALL SORTS OF FAR-REACHING DECISIONS IN THEIR ABSENCE...

AARGH... MY SECURITY PASS DOESN'T WORK! OH GOD... I MUST HAVE BEEN FIRED...

IT'S JUST BECAUSE COMPLIANCE WON'T ALLOW HIM ACCESS TO THIS PARTICULAR FLOOR...

PUTS THE FEAR OF GOD INTO THEM THOUGH...

Alex — PEATTIE + TAYLOR

THERE HAVE BEEN MANY INNOVATIONS IN THE CITY OFFICE IN THE YEARS SINCE I LAST WORKED IN ONE...

THESE DAYS EVERYTHING IS OPEN-PLAN, WHICH HAS REMOVED MUCH OF THE HIERARCHICAL, ELITIST AND DIVISIVE NATURE OF THE OLD WORKPLACE WITH ALL ITS LITTLE SEPARATE OFFICES...

AND THE INTRODUCTION OF MODERN ELECTRONIC COMMUNICATION TECHNIQUES HAS BROUGHT ABOUT A REVOLUTION IN THE WAY PEOPLE ARE ABLE TO TALK TO EACH OTHER...

"Thank goodness we've got instant messaging, now the boss sits within earshot..."

"Yes. How else would we be able to slag him off?"

TAP TAP

TAP TAP

Alex — PEATTIE + TAYLOR

IT'S ALWAYS TOUGH TAKING PART IN A "BEAUTY PARADE" TO WIN A NEW CLIENT'S BUSINESS...

ONE KNOWS ONE IS UP AGAINST ALL THE OTHER MAJOR INVESTMENT BANKS, EACH ONE OF US EQUIPPED WITH SLICK PRESENTATIONS TO PROVE THAT WE'RE THE BEST...

AND THEN, THIS MORNING, BY A TOTAL COINCIDENCE, A PIECE OF INFORMATION IS RELEASED WHICH HIGHLIGHTS HOW OUR BANK IS A MODEL OF 21ST CENTURY INVESTMENT BANKING PROFESSIONALISM AND PROPRIETY...

INDEED!

OUR TOP BLOODY ANALYST ISSUED A "SELL" NOTE ON THE STOCK OF THE COMPANY WE WERE PITCHING TO...

DO CHINESE WALLS PREVENT ME FROM WRINGING HIS NECK WHEN WE GET BACK?

Alex — PEATTIE + TAYLOR

AT £1,500 A BOTTLE PETRUS '90 IS BEYOND THE BUDGET OF MOST PEOPLE... BUT YOU'RE NOW SELLING IT BY THE GLASS, LUCY?

YES. WE STORE THE OPENED BOTTLE IN A SPECIAL NITROGEN CHAMBER WHICH PREVENTS THE WINE REACTING WITH THE OXYGEN IN THE AIR AND DETERIORATING...

IS THAT SO?... MOST INGENIOUS...

HMM... IT'S HEARTBREAKING TO THINK OF WINE OF THIS EXQUISITE VINTAGE BEING TRANSFORMED INTO SOMETHING QUITE ORDINARY AND UNREMARKABLE...

MMM.

SUCH AS A THREE COURSE MEAL FOR YOU AND FOUR CLIENTS?

EXACTLY... BUT A NECESSITY IF I'M GOING TO GET THIS THROUGH ON EXPENSES SO KINDLY DOCTOR THE BILL ACCORDINGLY...

email : alex-cartoon @ etgate.co.uk

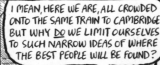

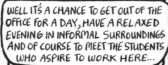

Row 1:

LOOK, RUPERT, YOU'VE GOT CLIVE SITTING IN AN OFFICE IN A CORRIDOR DOING ABSOLUTELY NOTHING.

I'VE GIVEN HIM A NON-JOB, ALEX... I WANT HIM TO RESIGN...

BUT DON'T FORGET OUR WHOLE CORPORATE BROKING TEAM WAS POACHED BY A RIVAL BANK LAST WEEK...

SURELY THIS CREATES AN OPPORTUNITY FOR CLIVE... I MEAN NONE OF THE VACANCIES HAVE YET BEEN FILLED... ISN'T IT AT LEAST WORTH GIVING IT A TRY?

WHAT, HAVE HIM SIT IN THERE AND PRESIDE OVER A TOTALLY EMPTY FLOOR?

I RECKON IT WOULD BE EVEN MORE DEMORALISING FOR HIM...

Row 2:

WHAT ARE YOU DOING, CLIVE?

JUST CHECKING MY WALLET AND POCKETS...

BRIDGET TENDS TO GO THROUGH THEM AT THE WEEKEND AND I WOULDN'T WANT HER TO FIND ANYTHING POTENTIALLY COMPROMISING...

I KNOW WHAT YOU MEAN...

WE ALL TEND TO ACCRUE ITEMS ABOUT OUR PERSON THAT MIGHT PROVE INCRIMINATING AND THAT WE WOULD WISH TO REMOVE BEFORE GOING HOME TO OUR WIVES...

BUT NOT NORMALLY OUR OWN BUSINESS CARDS...

IF SHE FINDS OUT I'VE BEEN DEMOTED TO HEAD OF "CLIENT FOCUS LIAISON"...

Row 3:

TOUGH NEW COMPLIANCE RULES HAVE STEPPED UP THE LEGAL OBLIGATIONS FACED BY A HEAD OF DEPARTMENT.

BOSSES ARE NOW HELD PERSONALLY ACCOUNTABLE FOR THEIR STAFF'S CONDUCT AND COULD ACTUALLY GO TO PRISON AS A RESULT OF ANY CRIMINAL ACTIONS BY THEIR UNDERLINGS...

WHEN ONE CONSIDERS THE NUMBER OF EMPLOYEES HEADS OF DEPARTMENT MAY BE RESPONSIBLE FOR, IT'S HARDLY SURPRISING THAT THEY MIGHT SOMETIMES CRACK UP UNDER THE PRESSURE...

REMEMBER: I'VE GOT MY EYE ON YOU, HELEN. I DON'T WANT YOU PILFERING POST-IT NOTES...

SOMETIMES I WISH IT WASN'T JUST YOU AND ME IN THIS DEPARTMENT, CLIVE...

HE'S THE ONE WE WANT TO RESIGN... NOT HER...

Row 4:

I DON'T KNOW WHERE I'D BE WITHOUT HELEN. SHE'S REALLY HELPED ME THROUGH THIS NIGHTMARISH SITUATION...

HERE I AM, HEADING UP THIS NON-DEPARTMENT CONSISTING OF JUST HER AND ME, WITH NO WORK AND NO CLIENTS. IT'D BE EASY FOR ME TO SINK INTO DESPONDENCY AND JUST SIT HERE AND VEGETATE ALL DAY...

BUT SHE'S A GREAT BELIEVER IN BEING PROACTIVE, SO SHE'S ENCOURAGED ME TO REGISTER ON VARIOUS COURSES THE BANK RUNS ON RETRAINING AND PERSONAL DEVELOPMENT...

WELL HOW ELSE AM I SUPPOSED TO GET HIM OUT OF THE WAY SO I CAN SLIP OUT AND INTERVIEW FOR OTHER JOBS?

Alex PEATTIE + TAYLOR

QUITE A FEW OF THE PEOPLE ON OUR TRADING FLOOR HAVE BEEN SENT FREE COPIES OF THIS NEW LIFESTYLE MAGAZINE... "TOP TRADER"...

THEY HAVE TO FILL IN AND RETURN A QUESTIONNAIRE ABOUT THEMSELVES TO RECEIVE FURTHER FREE ISSUES, WHICH MEANS THE PUBLISHERS CAN BUILD UP A DETAILED DATABASE OF WEALTHY AND SUCCESSFUL TRADERS...

VERY CLEVER.

BUT WOULD MOST CITY HIGH-FLIERS, WORKING IN A PRESSURISED, COMPETITIVE ENVIRONMENT LIKE THIS REALLY TAKE THE TIME TO REPLY?

WELL, IF THE MAGAZINE'S TARGETED AT THE RIGHT INDIVIDUALS...

LIKE GRADUATE TRAINEES, BACK OFFICE STAFF...

"TOP TRADER"? YOU'VE SENT YOUR RAG TO THE LITTLE SQUIT THAT SITS NEXT TO ME, BUT NOT TO ME! I GET PAID TEN TIMES WHAT HE DOES.

COULD YOU GIVE US YOUR EXACT DETAILS SIR?

I MOST CERTAINLY SHALL!

Alex PEATTIE + TAYLOR

LOOK, CLIVE, I'VE GOT TO COME CLEAN. RUPERT IS PAYING ME TO REVERSE HEADHUNT YOU.

WHAT?!

YOU MUST HAVE REALISED HE'S TRYING TO GET RID OF YOU. THAT'S WHY HE'S GOT YOU SITTING IN AN OFFICE DOING NOTHING... AND HE'S ASKED ME TO FIND EMPLOYMENT ELSEWHERE FOR YOU.

JUST TO GET ME TO RESIGN?

LOOK, I'M TELLING YOU THIS BECAUSE SOMETIMES IT'S BETTER TO STOP FIGHTING AGAINST THE TIDE AND JUST WALK AWAY FROM A JOB AND THE MONEY, WITH ONE'S PROFESSIONAL PRIDE AND DIGNITY INTACT...

SO THAT'S WHY I'M QUITTING THIS ASSIGNMENT... WHO AM I KIDDING? I'M NEVER GOING TO FIND ANYTHING FOR A HOPELESS CASE LIKE YOU...

OH THANK YOU SO MUCH...

Alex PEATTIE + TAYLOR

PART OF OUR JOB IN H.R. IS TO IMPROVE THE QUALITY OF THE BANK'S EMPLOYEES' LIVES...

THIS INVOLVES HELPING THEM MANAGE THE CONFLICT THAT OFTEN ARISES BETWEEN THEIR HOME AND OFFICE COMMITMENTS, WHICH IS WHY WE ORGANISE REGULAR SEMINARS ON WORK-LIFE BALANCE...

IRONICALLY SUCH IS THE PRESSURE OF THEIR JOBS THAT MANY PEOPLE ARE TOO BUSY TO ATTEND THESE SESSIONS, OR ELSE THEY SPEND THE WHOLE TIME IN THEM BEING DISTRACTED BY BUSINESS CALLS OR E-MAILS...

WHICH IS WHY WE DECIDED TO HOLD THEM ON A SATURDAY...

I CAN'T UNDERSTAND WHY PEOPLE AREN'T MORE APPRECIATIVE...

WORK LIFE BALANCE

Alex PEATTIE + TAYLOR

SO, HELEN, YOU'VE STARTED DATING A FELLOW MEMBER OF THE BANK'S STAFF. THANKS FOR INFORMING ME...

HEAD OF CLIENT FOCUS LIAISON

WELL REGULATIONS OBLIGE ME TO...

OF COURSE, AND AS YOUR BOSS I HAVE TO DECIDE WHETHER THE RELATIONSHIP CREATES A CONFLICT OF INTERESTS...

CAN I JUST SAY THAT I'VE HAD DALLIANCES WITH WORK COLLEAGUES BEFORE, CLIVE, BUT THIS IS DIFFERENT. THIS MAN MAKES ME HAPPY... IT'S THE REAL THING... I KNOW IT IS...

I MEAN, CONSIDERING THE TOTAL NON-JOB YOU HAVE THESE DAYS THERE'S NO WAY HE COULD BE JUST USING ME AS A WAY OF GAINING INFLUENCE WITH YOU...

AS I SAY, THANKS FOR INFORMING ME...

email : alex-cartoon @ etgate.co.uk

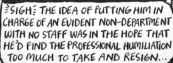

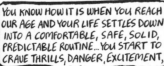

41

TOM? IT'S ALEX... WE'RE STUCK IN TRAFFIC... I'M AFRAID WE'RE NOT GOING TO BE THERE FOR ANOTHER 20 MINUTES... SORRY...

AT LEAST WITH MOBILE PHONES THESE DAYS ONE CAN ALWAYS LET SOMEONE KNOW WHEN ONE'S RUNNING LATE... I'M AFRAID HE SOUNDED VERY PUT OUT AND ANNOYED THOUGH...

OH DEAR.

WE'VE LEFT A BUSINESS COLLEAGUE SITTING IN A RESTAURANT ON HIS OWN FOR HALF AN HOUR AND HE'S CROSS ABOUT IT. THIS IS AN EXTREMELY EMBARRASSING SITUATION, ALEX...

INDEED IT IS...

NAMELY FOR HIM... BECAUSE HE CLEARLY HASN'T GOT A BLACKBERRY.

QUITE... THESE DAYS IT'S ASSUMED THAT NO ONE CARES IF YOU'RE LATE BECAUSE THEY CAN USE THE TIME TO CATCH UP ON THEIR E-MAILS...

I THOUGHT WE SHOULD GIVE THIS NEW RESTAURANT A TRY, CLIVE. IT'S THE LATEST EXPERIENCE FOR THE FASHIONABLE DINER...

IT'S WEIRD, ALEX... EATING IN TOTAL DARKNESS AND BEING SERVED BY BLIND WAITERS, BUT I MUST ADMIT THIS STARTER IS VERY GOOD...

AGREED, AND EVEN THOUGH ONE IS IS DEPRIVED OF VISUAL STIMULATION THE CULINARY EXPERIENCE IS IN NO WAY IMPAIRED BECAUSE ONE'S OTHER SENSES ARE CORRESPONDINGLY SHARPENED...

NOW, DID MY EARS JUST DETECT THE FAINT CLINK OF <u>CUTLERY</u>, CLIVE? YOU DO REALISE THAT ASPARAGUS IS EATEN WITH THE <u>FINGERS</u> IN POLITE SOCIETY?

BLAST...

SO, CLIVE, HOW ARE YOU FINDING THE GASTRONOMIC NOVELTY OF LUNCHING IN THE DARK?

MOST INTERESTING, ALEX...

WHAT'S REMARKABLE IS THE WAY THAT THE ABSENCE OF LIGHT IN THE RESTAURANT CAUSES ONE'S OTHER SENSES TO BE STIMULATED AND ENHANCED.

SENSES THAT HAVE A VITAL ROLE TO PLAY IN THE ASSESSMENT OF COOKING, SUCH AS SMELL FOR EXAMPLE...

YES. I AGREE, CLIVE...

SNIFF SNIFF I'M SURE THAT WAITER'S SEATED US AT THE BACK NEAR THE KITCHENS...

HOW INSULTING... WE'D BETTER MAKE A FUSS AND GET MOVED TO A DECENT TABLE...

SO, CLIVE, WHAT'S YOUR VERDICT ON EATING IN THE DARK?

I THINK I RATHER LIKE IT, ALEX...

AFTER ALL, YOU AND I LUNCH OUT MOST DAYS OF THE WEEK BUT THIS NEW RESTAURANT GIVES A TOTALLY DIFFERENT PERSPECTIVE ON THE EXPERIENCE...

HERE WE ARE, SEATED IN TOTAL OBSCURITY, SURROUNDED BY WHO KNOWS HOW MANY OTHER INVISIBLE DINERS... SOMEHOW IT HAS A VERY COMFORTING FEEL...

YES. I AGREE, CLIVE...

FOR ALL WE KNOW THE CLIENT WE'RE CLAIMING TO BE LUNCHING WITH MIGHT ACTUALLY <u>BE</u> HERE...

QUITE... SO I DON'T FEEL NEARLY SO GUILTY ABOUT PUTTING THIS THROUGH ON EXPENSES...

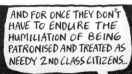

Strip 1

Alex PEATTIE + TAYLOR

WELL, ALEX, IT'S A SALUTARY EXPERIENCE BEING DEPENDENT ON THE VISUALLY-IMPAIRED STAFF WHO LED US INTO THIS PITCH DARK RESTAURANT...

INDEED, CLIVE.

THOSE PEOPLE WHO MIGHT ELSEWHERE FIND THEMSELVES AT A SOCIAL DISADVANTAGE ARE HERE ABLE TO EXIST ON AN EQUAL FOOTING WITH THEIR PEERS...

AND FOR ONCE THEY DON'T HAVE TO ENDURE THE HUMILIATION OF BEING PATRONISED AND TREATED AS NEEDY 2ND CLASS CITIZENS...

PEOPLE LIKE YOU, YOU MEAN, CLIVE, WHOSE ATTEMPTS TO ATTRACT THE ATTENTION OF THE WAITERS ARE USUALLY ROUTINELY IGNORED?

EXACTLY... FOR ONCE THERE'S NOTHING TO BE ASHAMED OF... AND NO ONE CAN SEE IT HAPPENING EITHER...

alex-cartoon @ etgate.co.uk

Strip 2

Alex PEATTIE + TAYLOR

YOU KNOW, ALEX, DINING IN TOTAL DARKNESS IS ACTUALLY QUITE A REFRESHING EXPERIENCE.

BEING IN A COMPLETELY LIGHTLESS ENVIRONMENT CREATES A MUCH MORE RELAXED AND CONDUCIVE ARENA FOR PROPER CONVERSATION...

I FIND I CAN CONCENTRATE ON WHAT I'M SAYING AND EXPRESS MYSELF WITH FAR GREATER FREEDOM, CONFIDENCE AND LACK OF INHIBITION...

BECAUSE THE GLOW FROM THE SCREEN OF YOUR BLACKBERRY GIVES AWAY EACH TIME YOU START SURREPTITIOUSLY CHECKING YOUR E-MAIL UNDER THE TABLE...

YOU MEAN I ACTUALLY HAVE TO SIT HERE AND _LISTEN_ TO YOU WITTERING ON, CLIVE?

alex-cartoon @ etgate.co.uk

Strip 3

Alex PEATTIE + TAYLOR

DANS LE NOIR?

WELL, I MUST SAY THAT WAS A MOST INTRIGUING GASTRONOMIC EXPERIENCE: DINING IN THE DARK...

IT WAS A VERY CHIC AND UPMARKET PLACE, THE QUALITY OF THE FOOD WAS EXCELLENT, NOT TO MENTION THE EXPERT SERVICE BY THE RESTAURANT'S BLIND AND PARTIALLY SIGHTED WAITERS

SO WHAT DO YOU THINK, ALEX? NOW THAT YOU'VE BEEN THERE ONCE, CAN YOU SEE YOURSELF GOING BACK?

THAT'S A NO-BRAINER, CLIVE...

TO AN ESTABLISHMENT WHERE BY DEFINITION NONE OF THE STAFF WOULD RECOGNISE ME...? WHAT WOULD BE THE POINT?

alex-cartoon @ etgate.co.uk

Strip 4

Alex PEATTIE + TAYLOR

SO YOU WANT TO RETAIN MY SERVICES AS A P.R. MAN TO KEEP NEWS OF YOUR MASSIVE EARNINGS OUT OF THE MEDIA?

YES PLEASE.

HEDGE FUNDS LIKE MINE HAVE DONE VERY WELL OF LATE... BUT IT BEHOVES PEOPLE LIKE ME TO BE DISCREET ABOUT IT IF WE DON'T WANT TO END UP GIVING ALL OUR PROFITS TO THE GOVERNMENT...

AT THIS PRESENT MOMENT OBVIOUSLY THERE ARE CERTAIN PEOPLE WHOSE ATTENTION WE DO NOT WISH TO BE DRAWN TO HOW MUCH MONEY WE'VE BEEN MAKING...

PEOPLE LIKE THE REGULATORS?

NO. LIKE MY WIFE... IF SHE READ ABOUT IT IN THE PAPERS SHE MIGHT DEMAND THAT I BOUGHT MYSELF A PEERAGE... THE STATUS-HUNGRY LITTLE MINX...

alex-cartoon @ etgate.co.uk

Alex PEATTIE + TAYLOR

OH HELLO, JÜRGEN...YOU _CAN_ MAKE A MEETING ON JUNE 20TH IN YOUR OFFICES? GREAT... SEE YOU THEN...

JUNE 20TH? THAT'S THE ENGLAND-SWEDEN WORLD CUP MATCH...

IT'S THE BIG GAME EVERY ENGLISHMAN WANTS TO SEE, CLIVE, AND WE'VE GOT TICKETS...OF COURSE ONE NEEDS A VALID EXCUSE TO BE OUT OF THE OFFICE AND IN A CONVENIENT LOCATION THAT DAY...

I'VE FIXED UP A CLIENT MEETING IN COLOGNE.

AND I'VE JUST ARRANGED ONE FOR MYSELF IN VIENNA...

ALEX...YOU DOLT.. VIENNA IS IN _AUSTRIA_... IT'S A TOTALLY DIFFERENT COUNTRY... THEY DIDN'T EVEN QUALIFY FOR THE WORLD CUP...

NIGHTMARE: EVERY FLIGHT FROM ENGLAND TO GERMANY ON JUNE 20TH IS FULLY BOOKED...

THERE'S LOTS OF AVAILABILITY ON LONDON-VIENNA. LIKEWISE ON VIENNA-COLOGNE FOR AFTER MY MEETING...

Alex PEATTIE + TAYLOR

MEMO TO SELF: I HAD TO REBUKE A STAFF MEMBER THIS MORNING...

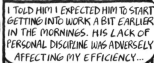

I TOLD HIM I EXPECTED HIM TO START GETTING INTO WORK A BIT EARLIER IN THE MORNINGS. HIS LACK OF PERSONAL DISCIPLINE WAS ADVERSELY AFFECTING MY EFFICIENCY...

I FIGURE THIS SHOULD IMPRESS ON MY DEPARTMENT THE WORK ETHIC I BELIEVE IN CULTIVATING...

I GOT A RIGHT B*LL*CKING OFF YOUR NEW BOSS WHEN I CAME INTO WORK THIS MORNING...

CANTEEN

HE GETS IN BEFORE _YOU_, AHMED? OH GOD..

YAWN

Alex PEATTIE + TAYLOR

ALEX AND I HAVE BEEN EXCHANGING ROMANTIC MESSAGES FOUR OR FIVE TIMES A DAY SINCE WE'VE BEEN SEEING EACH OTHER...

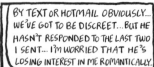

BY TEXT OR HOTMAIL OBVIOUSLY... WE'VE GOT TO BE DISCREET...BUT HE HASN'T RESPONDED TO THE LAST TWO I SENT... I'M WORRIED THAT HE'S LOSING INTEREST IN ME ROMANTICALLY.

IT HAPPENS, CAROLYN...

MEN INVARIABLY START TO TAKE WOMEN FOR GRANTED...YOU NEED TO FIND SOME WAY TO REKINDLE THE OLD EXCITEMENT... REMIND HIM OF WHAT FIRST ATTRACTED HIM TO YOU.

I DID...

I SENT HIM A REBUKE FROM MY _WORK_ E-MAIL... THIS BOUQUET ARRIVED WITHIN THE HOUR...

GOOD. NEVER LET HIM FORGET THAT YOU'RE A CLIENT AND HE CAN'T AFFORD TO P*SS YOU OFF...

Alex PEATTIE + TAYLOR

I'M TAKING PENNY TO THE NEW RESTAURANT THAT YOU AND I WENT TO LAST WEEK WHERE ONE EATS A DELICIOUS MEAL IN TOTAL DARKNESS SERVED BY BLIND WAITERS...

SHE'S ALWAYS MOCKED ME FOR BEING AN "EARLY ADOPTER" AND BEING THE FIRST TO BUY INTO ANY NEW EXPENSIVE GIMMICKY THING THAT CATCHES MY FANCY...

BUT I THINK FOR ONCE I'M GOING TO PROVE TO HER THAT AT LEAST ONE OF MY DISCOVERIES ISN'T JUST A USELESS WORTHLESS FAD OF NO INTRINSIC MERIT...

THERE, PENNY! I TOLD YOU THESE NIGHT VISION GOGGLES I BOUGHT FROM THE "INNOVATIONS" CATALOGUE IN 1987 WOULD COME IN USEFUL ONE DAY...

ALEX, YOU DO REALISE NO ONE ELSE CAN SEE YOU WEARING THEM..?

WHAT?! REALLY?! OH, YES. DAMN.

Alex PEATTIE + TAYLOR

WHO WAS THAT YOU WERE CHATTING AWAY TO SO AMIABLY?

OH SOME COLD CALLER TRYING TO SELL ME INSURANCE.

HE WAS CLEARLY BASED IN MUMBAI OR BANGALORE OR SOMEWHERE AND HAD BEEN GIVEN A LIST OF CONVERSATIONAL TOPICS TO BUTTER UP U.K. CUSTOMERS WITH...

SO YOU TALKED FOR TEN MINUTES ABOUT THE WEATHER AND SOAP OPERAS?

WELL, CLIVE, WHAT POSSIBLE AREA OF MUTUAL INTEREST COULD THERE BE BETWEEN ME AND SOME TELESALES WORKER IN INDIA?

ER...THE CRICKET THAT'S GOING ON OUT THERE AT THE MOMENT?

EXACTLY. IT MUST HAVE REALLY IRKED HIM HAVING TO REFRAIN FROM GLOATING, ESPECIALLY AS I HUNG UP AS SOON AS HE STARTED HIS SALES PITCH...

Alex PEATTIE + TAYLOR

SO, SARA, HOW'S THE MOVE TO MEGABANK YOU'RE NEGOTIATING FOR ME GOING?

FINE, TIM. THEY'RE VERY KEEN TO RECRUIT YOU. IN FACT THE HEAD OF DEPARTMENT WANTS TO INTERVIEW YOU THIS WEEK..

GREAT...

HIS NAME IS CYRUS...THE ONLY PROBLEM IS THAT HE'S GOT AN INCREDIBLY BUSY DIARY. HOWEVER HE COULD FIT YOU IN FOR FIFTEEN MINUTES AT 7.45 ON THURSDAY...

YEAH, I COULD DO THAT..

WELL MY TIME'S UP... THANKS FOR COMING IN, TIM... WHERE ARE YOU HEADED NOW?

ER, BACK TO LONDON I SUPPOSE...

Alex PEATTIE + TAYLOR

LOOK, CYRUS, I'M GRATEFUL OBVIOUSLY TO BE CONSIDERED FOR THIS JOB AT MEGABANK...

BUT DID WE REALLY HAVE TO DO THE INTERVIEW ON A PLANE?

SORRY, TIM, BUT I'M ON A VERY TIGHT SCHEDULE...THIS WAS THE ONLY WINDOW I HAD..

BUT I HAD TO TAKE THIS FLIGHT JUST TO GET FIFTEEN MINUTES OF YOUR TIME...I'VE NOW GOT TO SIT ON IT THE REST OF THE WAY TO FRANKFURT.

I APPRECIATE THAT, BUT THE SITUATION IS NOT EXACTLY IDEAL FOR ME...

NOW IF YOU WOULDN'T MIND SWITCHING SEATS WITH THE GUY IN 14B... HE'S NEXT UP...

Alex PEATTIE + TAYLOR

RIGHT ... I THINK I'VE SET UP THIS AUDIO CONFERENCE ... COULD EVERYONE JUST SAY HELLO SO I KNOW YOU'RE ALL THERE?

OF COURSE IT WOULD BE SIMPLER WITH A VIDEO CONFERENCE, BUT THAT'S NEVER REALLY CAUGHT ON FOR SOME REASON...

YES... FUNNY THAT, CLIVE...

OH, HELLO, ALEX...

THOUGH, ALEX, I SUPPOSE IT WOULD BE NICE FOR US ALL TO SEE THE LUXURY VILLA YOU'RE STAYING AT OUT THERE IN BARBADOS... SORRY TO DISTURB YOUR BREAK... HOW'S THE WEATHER THERE?

BEAUTIFUL, THANKS...

AND HOW'S THE WEATHER WHERE YOU ARE, CAROLYN?

ER... A BIT OVERCAST.

NO, CLIVE, I CAN'T SEE WHAT USE VIDEO-CONFERENCING WOULD BE TO ANYONE...

ALEX WENT ON HOLIDAY WITH HIS MISTRESS...

(WHO WAS ALSO HIS CLIENT)

CYRUS DID NOT TAKE A HOLIDAY...

BUT HE DID RUN THE LONDON MARATHON...

Strip 1

SO, CYRUS, HOW DID YOU ENJOY RUNNING THE LONDON MARATHON?

IT WAS A GREAT EXPERIENCE IN MANY WAYS, ALEX.

THOUGH I GOTTA SAY I WAS A LITTLE DISAPPOINTED WITH MY FINISHING TIME: 5 HOURS 48 MINUTES...

THAT'S A LITTLE ON THE SLOW SIDE, CONSIDERING HOW FIT YOU ARE...

WELL, THEY SAY THAT A MARATHON IS RUN IN THE MIND, ALEX... AND I GUESS I JUST DIDN'T HAVE THE MENTAL TOUGHNESS OR WILLPOWER REQUIRED...

WHAT, TO RUN PAST THE OFFICE HERE AT MILE 19 WITHOUT POPPING IN?

I ALWAYS LIKE TO PUT IN A COUPLA HOURS AT MY DESK ON A SUNDAY MORNING...

Strip 2

LOOK, PAUL, WHAT I'M ABOUT TO TELL YOU MAY CAUSE YOU TO DOWNGRADE THE AMOUNT OF BUSINESS YOU GIVE MY BANK...

AS YOU MAY BE AWARE, WE HAVE AN INTERNAL SYSTEM BY WHICH WE RATE CLIENTS AS ALPHA, BETA OR GAMMA ACCORDING TO THEIR VALUE TO THE BANK...

YES...

WELL, I'M VERY SORRY TO TELL YOU THAT YOUR COMPANY'S RATING HAS RECENTLY BEEN REASSESSED. I'M AFRAID IT'S BAD NEWS...

OH NO...

YES... WE'VE MADE YOU AN ALPHA...

SO I'LL NOW HAVE TO SIT THROUGH LOADS OF TEDIOUS MEETINGS WITH YOUR SENIOR MANAGEMENT?

OUR GLOBAL HEAD OF CLIENT RELATIONS IS FLYING IN TO SEE YOU TOMORROW...

Strip 3

THE OPENING OF THIS RESTAURANT WHERE CUSTOMERS DINE IN THE DARK...

DANS LE NOIR?

DINE IN THE DARK

HAS BEEN A REAL BOON TO BLIND PEOPLE LIKE US...

QUITE. OUR SKILLS AS WAITERS ARE HIGHLY PRIZED HERE...

IT'S GOOD TO REMIND PEOPLE THAT BEING BLIND ISN'T NECESSARILY A DISADVANTAGE IN LIFE...

IN THE ANIMAL KINGDOM FOR EXAMPLE BATS ARE ABLE TO NAVIGATE VERY ACCURATELY BY USING THEIR ULTRASONIC HEARING TO TUNE INTO A SERIES OF CLICKS.

CLICK CLICK CLICK

I HATE IT WHEN CUSTOMERS DO THAT TO ATTRACT OUR ATTENTION...

OI! WAITER!

MAKE SURE YOU SPILL SOME HOT SOUP ON HIS LAP BY MISTAKE ON PURPOSE...

Strip 4

HAVING A BLACKBERRY MEANS A MANAGER CAN STILL DO HIS JOB THESE DAYS, EVEN WHEN HE'S ABROAD ON A BUSINESS TRIP...

OF COURSE IT'S FRUSTRATING THAT THEY CAN'T BE USED ON PLANES, WHICH MEANS I'LL BE OUT OF DIRECT CONTACT WITH MY TEAM FOR THE TWO-HOUR DURATION OF THIS FLIGHT,

BUT MY TIME IS NOT WASTED BECAUSE I CAN STILL USE IT IN OFFLINE MODE TO COMPOSE E-MAILS FOR SENDING LATER, WHICH OF COURSE IS VERY PRACTICAL...

CAVE! CYRUS'S PLANE HAS JUST LANDED - I'VE JUST GOT 25 E-MAILS FROM HIM...

ME TOO... CAN WE FIT IN ONE MORE GLASS OF WINE AND STILL BEAT HIM BACK TO THE OFFICE...?

BLEEP BLEEP

Row 1

WHERE'S CLIVE? / HE'S GONE OVER TO STARBUCKS FOR AN OFF-THE-RECORD CHAT WITH A GERMAN CLIENT OF HIS...

BRUNO'S GOT A SPARE CORPORATE TICKET FOR THE ENGLAND V. PARAGUAY WORLD CUP GAME ON SATURDAY AND CLIVE'S HOPING TO GET HIMSELF AN INVITE. / BUT THERE IS NOTHING ILLEGAL IN THAT...

I THOUGHT THOSE CLANDESTINE COFFEE SHOP MEETINGS WERE FOR WHEN YOU DO NOT WISH WHAT YOU SAY TO BE OVERHEARD OR RECORDED BECAUSE IT MIGHT PROVE COMPROMISING TO YOU / YES THAT'S CORRECT...

AS YOU KNOW, BRUNO, I LOVE ANY OPPORTUNITY TO VISIT FRANKFURT... THAT BEAUTIFUL, CULTURAL AND... ER, STIMULATING METROPOLIS OF YOURS... / YA! KEEP GOING... I HAVE WAITED YEARS TO HEAR YOU SAY THIS ABOUT MY CITY...

Row 2

SO, CLIVE, A ROCK FESTIVAL FOR HEDGE FUND MANAGERS BASED ON WOODSTOCK. WHAT DO YOU THINK?

IT'S ODD, ALEX. I MEAN WOODSTOCK WAS ALL ABOUT A GENERATION THAT REJECTED CAPITALISTIC MATERIALISM AND WANTED TO OVERTURN THE VALUES OF SOCIETY... / MAIN STAGE THE WHO

BUT LOOK AT THESE PEOPLE... I DOUBT THERE'S A SINGLE PERSON HERE WHO COULD BE SAID TO BE DISGRUNTLED WITH THE SOCIAL ORDER...

THIS IS ALL WRONG, PETE. THESE PEOPLE ARE ALL RICHER THAN US... / YEAH, WHAT'S GOING ON, ROG? WE'RE SUPPOSED TO BE THE SMUG, PREENING, SELF-INDULGENT MULTI-MILLIONAIRES... / THE WHO

Row 3

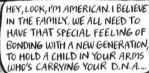

I THOUGHT YOU WOULDN'T APPROVE OF ME BECOMING A FATHER, CYRUS... THAT YOU'D THINK IT WOULD DISTRACT ME FROM MY WORK... / DON'T BE SILLY, DAN... / DISPOSABLE NAPPIES

HEY, LOOK, I'M AMERICAN. I BELIEVE IN THE FAMILY, WE ALL NEED TO HAVE THAT SPECIAL FEELING OF BONDING WITH A NEW GENERATION, TO HOLD A CHILD IN YOUR ARMS WHO'S CARRYING YOUR D.N.A...

YOU'RE GONNA BE GREAT WITH KIDS, I CAN TELL, DAN... WATCHING THEM GROW UP, TEACHING THEM TO PLAY FOOTBALL, FISH, SAIL... YOU'VE GOT ALL THAT AHEAD OF YOU NOW... / DISPOSABLE NAPPIES

...IN JUST 25 YEARS OR SO WHEN YOU'RE RETIRED AND FINALLY HAVE FREE TIME TO SPEND WITH YOUR GRANDCHILDREN... / IN THE MEANTIME I EXPECT YOU BACK IN THE OFFICE AT 6.15 TOMORROW MORNING... / GULP

Row 4

CYRUS AND CLIVE... YOU ARE ALWAYS ARGUING OVER NUANCES OF THE ENGLISH LANGUAGE AND CULTURE...

IT IS IRONIC: YOU ARE BOTH ANGLO-SAXONS, BUT MAYBE YOU NEED TO ADMIT THAT THE BRITISH AND THE AMERICANS HAVE LESS IN COMMON THAN YOU THOUGHT...

IS IT SUCH A BAD THING? IN FRANCE WE HAVE A SAYING: "VIVE LA DIFFERENCE!" HOW DO YOU SAY THIS IN ENGLISH? / NICE POINT, CHRISTIAN...

I GUESS WE SAY: LET'S HAPPIFY THE NON-COMMUNALITY... / NO... NO... WE DO NOT SAY THAT... EVER. UNDER ANY CIRCUMSTANCES...

Alex PEATTIE + TAYLOR

MOST AIRLINES ARE NOW INSTALLING PHONES ON ALL THEIR PLANES... BUT IT'S NOT NECESSARILY POPULAR WITH BUSINESS PEOPLE...

FOR MANY OF US, THE DURATION OF AN AIR FLIGHT CAN BE THE ONLY RESPITE WE GET FROM THE DEMANDS OF OUR WORKING LIVES ...THE CHANCE JUST TO RELAX...

SO THE OCCASIONAL BUSINESS TRIP ON AN AIRLINE THAT ISN'T EQUIPPED WITH PHONES OR E-MAIL CAN BE A RELIEF. TOMORROW NIGHT FOR EXAMPLE I'M LOOKING FORWARD TO GETTING SOME REST...

BUT YOU'RE NOT GOING ON A BUSINESS TRIP TOMORROW...

NO BUT MY AMERICAN BOSS CYRUS IS ... WHICH MEANS HE WON'T BE ABLE TO PHONE ME FOR SIX WHOLE HOURS...

RING RING

OH GOD. NO DOUBT THAT'S HIM NOW...

Alex PEATTIE + TAYLOR

OUR NEW AMERICAN HEAD OF DEPARTMENT IS A FUNDAMENTALIST CHRISTIAN. HE ACTUALLY DISPUTES THE THEORY OF EVOLUTION...

SOMEONE LIKE YOU, MYLES, WHO'S GOT A DOCTORATE IN MOLECULAR BIOLOGY AND WHO'S SPENT 15 YEARS AS A RESEARCH SCIENTIST MUST FEEL STRONGLY ABOUT THIS.

I DO, CLIVE.

WHEN ONE THINKS OF THE SUBTLE WAYS HIS SORT HAVE OF UNDER-MINING CLASSICAL RATIONALIST THINKING AND OBSTRUCTING SCIENTISTS LIKE YOU IN DOING YOUR JOBS...

YES...

BY PAYING US TWENTY TIMES AS MUCH TO WORK AS BIOTECH ANALYSTS IN THEIR BANKS...BLOODY MARVELLOUS. I CAN'T WAIT TO SHOW THE LADS BACK AT THE LAB MY PORSCHE...

Alex PEATTIE + TAYLOR

OUR DEPARTMENT'S ALLOCATION OF TICKETS FOR ENGLAND'S CRUNCH WORLD CUP GAME AGAINST SWEDEN HAS BEEN PATHETIC...

JUST FOUR TICKETS...

AND EACH ONE OF US HAS VALUABLE CLIENTS WHO'D JUMP AT THE CHANCE TO GO. IT'S A TOUGH ONE TO RESOLVE.

YES, BUT IN THE END THE BANK'S INTERESTS ARE PARAMOUNT. THIS IS ALL ABOUT GENERATING GOODWILL FROM OUR CLIENTS AND SO, SADLY, SOMEONE HAS TO LOSE OUT...

THE DISAFFECTION FROM THE CLIENTS WHO HEARD WE HADN'T CHOSEN THEM TO BE OUR GUESTS WOULD HAVE OUTWEIGHED THE BENEFIT FROM THOSE WE DID INVITE...

SO BETTER TO TAKE NO ONE AT ALL...

Alex PEATTIE + TAYLOR

I DON'T UNDERSTAND CYRUS AT ALL... I MEAN THE MAN'S AN AUTOMATON WHO ONLY LIVES TO WORK...

YET AT THE SAME TIME HE KEEPS LECTURING US ON FAMILY VALUES AND HOW WE SHOULDN'T ALLOW OUR WORK TO INTRUDE ON OUR TIME WITH OUR LOVED ONES...

HIS MESSAGE SEEMS STRAIGHTFORWARD TO ME, CLIVE...

IT'S JUST A GENTLE WARNING THAT WE CITY BANKERS ARE RUNNING THE RISK OF MISSING OUT ON SOMETHING IMPORTANT, VALUABLE AND LIFE-ENHANCING.

OUR FAMILIES?

NO: OUR BONUSES... HE'S CLEARLY HINTING THAT THE WAY THE MARKETS ARE GOING WE MAY NOT BE GETTING ANY...

SO THERE'S NO POINT IN PUTTING ON A SHOW OF WORKING LATE EVERY NIGHT...? I SEE...

Strip 1

Panel 1: WELL IT'S NICE TO SEE YOU OUT WITH YOUR WIFE FOR ONCE, RATHER THAN YOUR MISTRESS, ALEX... / SHH.

Panel 2: LOOK, I KNOW CAROLYN'S BECOME MY DE FACTO COMPANION AT SOCIAL EVENTS THESE DAYS BUT SHE'S AN IMPORTANT CLIENT OF THE BANK AND I NEED TO ENTERTAIN HER...

Panel 3: BUT OBVIOUSLY I'D NEVER NOT TAKE PENNY TO LADIES' DAY AT ROYAL ASCOT. SHE SO LOVES ALL THE OLD-FASHIONED TRADITION AND FORMALITY OF IT...THE THINGS SHE GETS TO WEAR...

Panel 4: SUCH AS A NAME BADGE SAYING "MRS ALEXANDER MASTERLEY"...? / HELLO, I THINK WE'VE MET BEFORE... YOU'RE CAROLYN AREN'T YOU? / ER... NO, ACTUALLY...

Strip 2

Panel 1: SO YOU'VE BEEN ALLOWED TO HAVE THE WORLD CUP ON THE TVs IN THE TRADING FLOOR, GARRY?

Panel 2: WELL MANAGEMENT CAN'T AFFORD TO HAVE US SKIVING OFF TO THE WINE BAR TO WATCH THE FOOTBALL AT A TIME WHERE THE WEAKNESS OF THE GLOBAL ECONOMY HAS MADE THE MARKETS HIGHLY VOLATILE...

Panel 3: WE'RE TRADERS AND IT'S IMPORTANT FOR US TO BE AT OUR DESKS WHERE WE'RE PROPERLY EQUIPPED TO REACT TO THE NEWS AND EVENTS AS THEY UNFOLD...

Panel 4: I WANT TO CLOSE OFF MY POSITION ON UKRAINIAN CORNERS AND BUY TUNISIAN THROW INS... / I'M SHORTING SAUDI YELLOW CARDS AT 2.2... / I'LL GO LONG ON GOALKEEPER PUNCHES... / SO I SEE... / SPORT BET

Strip 3

Panel 1: LOOK...THERE'S ALEX AT WIMBLEDON WITH CAROLYN THAT CLIENT OF HIS... / HE WENT WITHOUT YOU, PENNY?

Panel 2: WELL, HE CLAIMED THAT HIS BANK ONLY HAD TWO TICKETS AND THAT IT WAS IMPERATIVE HE INVITE HER AS HE'S DESPERATE TO KEEP HER BUSINESS...

Panel 3: HAVING SAID THAT, I MUST ADMIT IT STILL COMES AS SOMETHING OF A SHOCK TO ME TO SEE HIM SITTING THERE IN THE CENTRE COURT...

Panel 4: WHAT, RATHER THAN BEING IN THE HOSPITALITY TENT WATCHING THE WORLD CUP? / HEE-HEE, YES... HE'S OBVIOUSLY TOO SCARED TO RISK IT WITH HER... / A COUPLE THERE OBVIOUSLY ENJOYING THIS LADIES' DOUBLES MATCH...

Strip 4

Panel 1: BACK HOME WE PLAY FOOTBALL, CLIVE. THAT'S A SPORT WITH GENUINE CORE TEAM FOCUS AND STRATEGIC GEOGRAPHIES. / AMERICAN FOOTBALL, CYRUS...

Panel 2: OBSCURE, OVER-COMPLEX AND JARGON-RIDDEN, LIKE EVERYTHING IN THE USA; WHEREAS SOCCER—AS YOU INSIST ON CALLING IT—IS A GAME OF CLASSICAL SIMPLICITY...

Panel 3: SO HOW COME I DON'T GET IT? HOLD ON... THAT GUY TRIPPED THE OTHER GUY... THAT'S A PENALTY, RIGHT? / NO, IT'S A FREE KICK.

Panel 4: SO HOW COME IT'S NOT A PENALTY? WHAT WAS THE REFEREE THINKING? / IT WAS OUTSIDE THE BOX, CYRUS.

Panel 5: "OUTSIDE THE BOX" THINKING, EH? I LIKE IT! MAYBE I CAN RELATE TO THIS GAME AFTER ALL...

Alex PEATTIE + TAYLOR

SO IT'S AGREED: THE BANK NEEDS TO DISTANCE ITSELF FROM ANY INTERNET GAMING COMPANY FLOATS WE'VE DONE...

RUPERT STERLING DIRECTOR

WE DON'T WANT TO FALL FOUL OF THE U.S. PROSECUTORS...

WHO DO THEY THINK THEY ARE? RIDING IN TO CLEAN UP OUR TOWN LIKE WYATT EARP...

THEY'RE STILL LIVING IN THE WILD WEST... THEY THINK THIS IS DODGE CITY OR DEADWOOD GULCH... OR... OR...

...ER... TOMBSTONE...?

AAARGH...

SPORT PUNT .COM

FIND OUT HOW MANY MORE OF THESE THINGS WE'VE GOT AND BIN THEM ALL...

Alex PEATTIE + TAYLOR

DON'T WORRY, CYRUS... WE'RE USED TO INDUSTRIAL ACTION HERE IN BRITAIN. MANAGEMENT JUST NEEDS TO PLAY A WAITING GAME.

WHAT TRADITIONALLY HAPPENS IS THAT ONCE THE WINTER WEATHER SETS IN, THE STRIKERS' RESOLVE STARTS TO CRUMBLE AND THEY BEGIN GRADUALLY DRIFTING BACK TO WORK...

BEING IN THEIR COSY WORKPLACE SEEMS A PREFERABLE OPTION TO THEM THAN FACING UP TO THE INHOSPITABLE CONDITIONS OUT IN THE STREET...

BUT IT'S SUMMER AND THESE GUYS ARE BANKERS.

EXACTLY.

I CAN'T TAKE ANY MORE OF THIS HEATWAVE, CHAPS... I'M GOING BACK TO MY NICE AIR-CONDITIONED OFFICE...

MEGABANK

SWEAT

SCAB!

BEAT BEAT

PANT

DRIP

OFFICIAL PICKET

Alex PEATTIE + TAYLOR

I'VE JUST HAD MY WIFE ON THE PHONE, NICK. SHE SAYS YOU'RE WORKING OUR SON CHRISTOPHER TOO HARD...

WELL, IT'S TRUE I'VE ASKED HIM TO RE-INDEX OUR WHOLE PRESS CUTTINGS DATABASE, WHICH WILL ENTAIL HIM REMAINING IN THE OFFICE UNTIL QUITE LATE TONIGHT...

BUT HE'S DOING WORK EXPERIENCE, ALEX. IT'S JUST A QUESTION OF WHETHER YOU WANT THIS SUMMER INTERNSHIP TO GIVE HIM A PROPER INSIGHT INTO WHAT'S INVOLVED IN REAL WORKING LIFE IN THE CITY...

AHEM... ER... NO... OBVIOUSLY NOT...

EXACTLY... I WANTED TO AVOID HIM TAGGING ALONG WITH ME... I'LL SEE YOU DOWN THERE IN 10 MINUTES...

Lap Dancing Club

Alex PEATTIE + TAYLOR

I HAVEN'T BEEN TO COWES FOR A FEW YEARS SO YOU'D BETTER REMIND ME HOW IT ALL WORKS...

OK, ALEX.

MEGABANK

MEGABANK

MEGABANK!

IT'S A SIMPLE COURSE WE HAVE TO STEER ROUND. SOME OF THE MARKER BUOYS MAY SEEM NEW BUT THEY'VE PROBABLY JUST BEEN RENAMED BY THEIR SPONSORS.

SORRY...?

MEGA BANK

MEGA BANK

I SAID, EVEN THOUGH A FEW OF THEM MIGHT BE UNFAMILIAR, IT'S ESSENTIALLY THE SAME OLD BUOYS AND WE HAVE TO WORK OUR WAY ROUND THEM ALL...

NO PROBLEM...

MEGA BANK

THE SAME OLD BOYS, EH? GLAD TO HEAR IT... YES, I'M LOOKING FORWARD TO THE CHAMPAGNE TENT... NOW WHAT ABOUT THIS STUPID RACE WE HAVE TO DO FIRST?

MEGA BANK

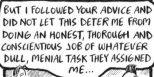